Marvelous Manners Award

This award recognizes your polite
and thoughtful behavior in our classroom.

Thank you for showing respect to others.
You should feel really proud of yourself!

Sincerely, _____ Date _____

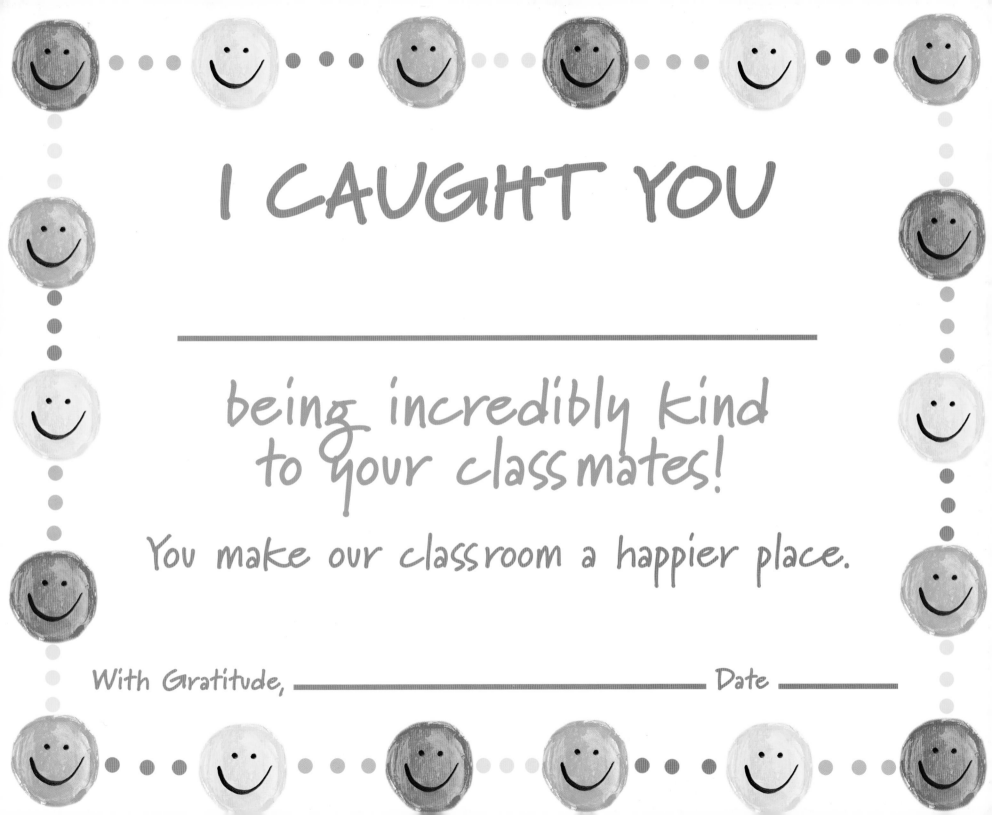

I CAUGHT YOU

_____

being incredibly kind
to your classmates!

You make our classroom a happier place.

With Gratitude, _____ Date _____

Stellar Speller Award

This is to certify that

_____

is a super speller!

All your hard work and practice has helped you earn this award. It's great to see you trying.

Keep up the wonderful work!

Sincerely, _____ Date _____

Awesome Kid Award

This is to certify that

_____

is a super, duper kid and a joy to have in class.
Thanks for being terrific you!

Sincerely, _____ Date _____

Homework Hero

You have been doing a great job getting your homework done.

This award recognizes your hard work at both school AND home.

Way to go!

Sincerely, _____ Date _____

I Believe in You!

This certificate officially recognizes my confidence in your abilities! You're a super kid and I know you can do great things. Keep trying, keep working, keep believing in you too!

Sincerely, _____ Date _____

Super Reader Award

This award is presented to

_____

you keep getting better and better.
Congratulations to you!

Sincerely, _____ Date _____

HOORAY FOR YOU!

This certificate is awarded with pride to

_____

for being such a great classroom helper.
Thank you so much for your super
attitude and cooperation.

Sincerely, _____ Date_____

Marvelous Manners Award

This award recognizes your polite
and thoughtful behavior in our classroom.

Thank you for showing respect to others.
You should feel really proud of yourself!

Sincerely, _____ Date _____

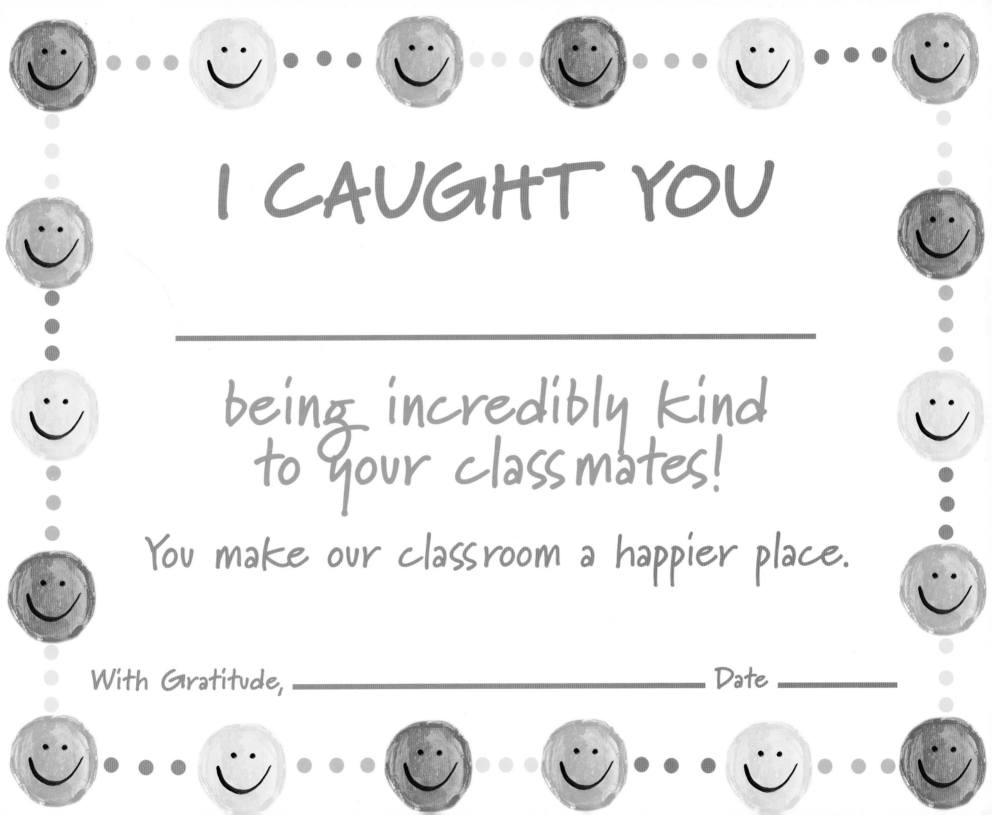

I CAUGHT YOU

being incredibly kind
to your classmates!

You make our classroom a happier place.

With Gratitude, _____ Date _____

A+ for Effort!

You've been trying so hard at everything you do.
Just wanted you to know that I've noticed your effort.

I'm so proud of you and you should be, too!

Sincerely, _____ Date _____

Stellar Speller Award

This is to certify that

_____

is a super speller!

All your hard work and practice has helped you
earn this award. It's great to see you trying.

Keep up the wonderful work!

Sincerely, _____ Date _____

Awesome Kid Award

This is to certify that

_____

is a super, duper kid and a joy to have in class.
Thanks for being terrific you!

Sincerely, _____ Date _____

Homework Hero

You have been doing a great job
getting your homework done.

This award recognizes
your hard work at both
school AND home.

Way to go!

Sincerely, _____ Date _____

I Believe in You!

This certificate officially recognizes my confidence in your abilities! You're a super kid and I know you can do great things. Keep trying, keep working, keep believing in you too!

Sincerely, _____ Date _____